Robert Pizzo's AMAZING ANIMAL ALPHABET

★ ★ ★ ★ ★ ★ ★

COLORING BOOK

How would you color a Crabby Crab Cabbie? How would you ornament an Outlandish, Oboe-playing Octopus? In his book *The Amazing Animal Alphabet of Twenty-Six Tongue Twisters* (Pomegranate, 2013), artist and author Robert Pizzo assembled a cast of crazy critters to star in twenty-six tiny, tongue-twisting tales—one for every letter of the alphabet. He did the coloring in that book himself, setting his maniacal menagerie in a collection of captivatingly chaotic, brightly colored contexts. Now it's your turn: this coloring book offers Robert's same twenty-six tongue-torturing tableaux in black-and-white line drawings that cry out for creative coloring! Should the Abstract Artist Alligator be gargoyle green? Or petunia pink? Should the Zeppole-eating Zebra sport his standard stripes? Or perhaps purple polka dots? It's entirely up to you. So grab your greens and round up your reds! Lasso your lavenders and break out the blues! The ABC's have never been so fun. And if you just can't stop when you've finished Robert's alphabet—keep going! An additional blank coloring page at the back awaits your boundlessly brilliant imagination. Just remember, when all the pages are colored and the crayons are put away, you still won't truly be finished until you can say each of Robert's tongue twisters three times fast. Better start practicing! Better start practicing! Better start practicing!

Pomegranate

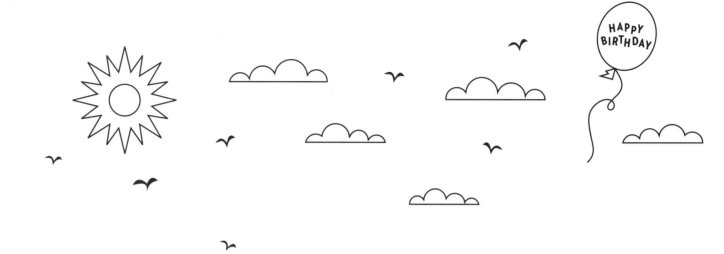

Pomegranate Communications, Inc.
19018 NE Portal Way, Portland OR 97230
800 227 1428   www.pomegranate.com

© 2014 Robert Pizzo

Catalog No. CB154

Designed by Tristen Jackman

Printed in Korea

24 23 22 21 20 19 18 17 16 15   11 10 9 8 7 6 5 4 3 2

Distributed by Pomegranate Europe Ltd.
Unit 1, Heathcote Business Centre, Hurlbutt Road
Warwick, Warwickshire CV34 6TD, UK
[+44] 0 1926 430111
sales@pomeurope.co.uk

This product is in compliance with the Consumer Product Safety Improvement Act of 2008 (CPSIA)
and any subsequent amendments thereto. A General Conformity Certificate concerning
Pomegranate's compliance with the CPSIA is available on our website at www.pomegranate.com,
or by request at 800 227 1428. For additional CPSIA-required tracking details, contact Pomegranate
at 800 227 1428.

Big Brown Bull Blasts off a Badly Built Bright Blue Bicycle.

OFF DUTY

TAXI

Crabby Crab Cabbie Cruises in a Cool Classic Checker Cab.

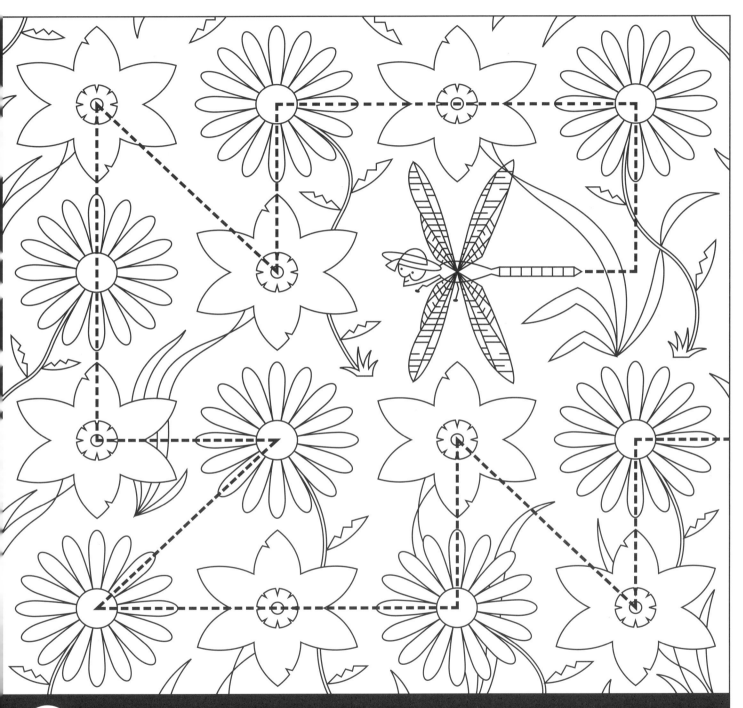

Delicate Dainty Dragonfly Darts from Daisies to Daffodils.

Enormously Elegant Elephant wears Electric Easter-Egg Earrings.

Fantastically Fearless Frog Flaunts a Funny Fake-Fur Fez.

Gigantic Gawky Gorilla Gets to Go in a Goofy Green Go-kart.

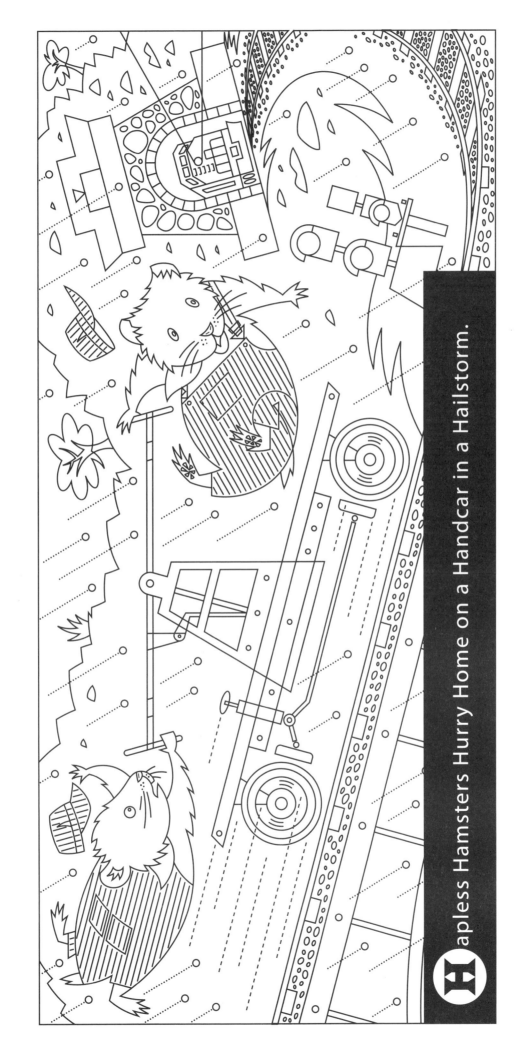

Hapless Hamsters Hurry Home on a Handcar in a Hailstorm.

Fig. 1.

Incredible Inventor Impala Imagines Ingeniously Inspired Ideas.

J aunty Jazzy Jackrabbit Jumps over a Junky Jalopy Jeep.

 arate Kid Kangaroo Keeps Kicking a King-sized Knish Kabob.

 azy Little Lion Lounges Leisurely on Lake Lucerne.

Mad Messy Monkeys Make too Much Macaroni on the Moon.

Natty Nightingale Neatly Nibbles Nachos in her Nest.

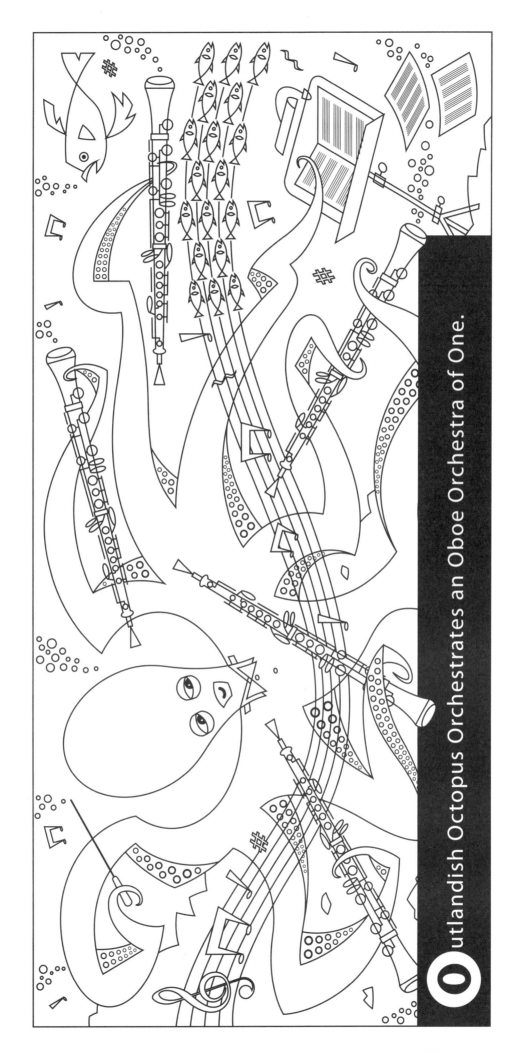

Outlandish Octopus Orchestrates an Oboe Orchestra of One.

Penguins Play Ping-Pong with Pretty Polka-dotted Paddles.

Quirky Queen bee Quietly Quilts a Quilt Quite nicely.

Rowdy Raunchy Red Rooster Really Rocks 'Round the clock.

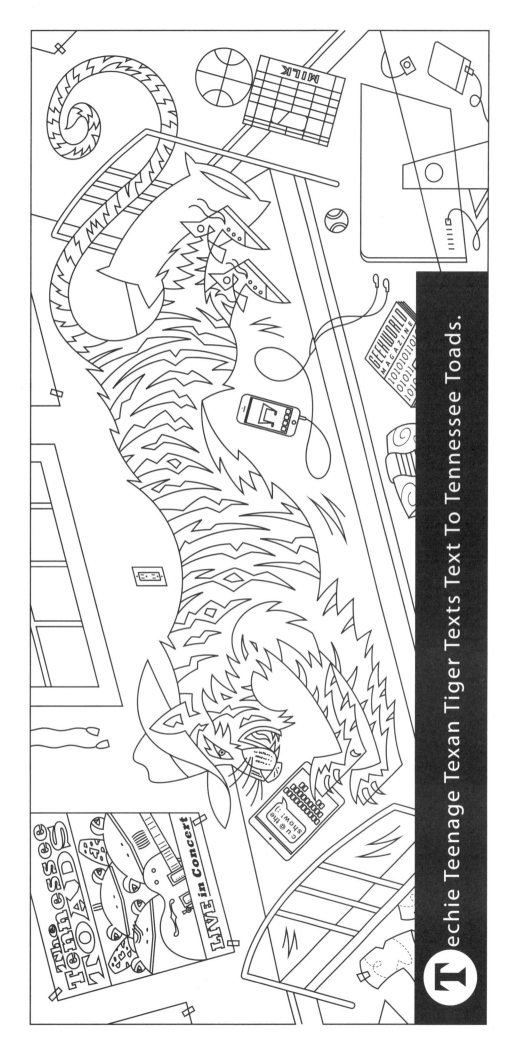

Techie Teenage Texan Tiger Texts Text To Tennessee Toads.

Uh, oh! Umbrellabird Utterly Underestimates Unearthly UFOs.

 agabond Viper Vacations in a Valise in Vulture Valley.

X-ray fish goes eXploring on eXceptionally eXotic eXciting eXpeditions.

 odeling Yammering Yachtsman Yak Yanks a Yolky Yellow Yo-Yo.

Zeppole-eating Zebra Zings on a Zippy Zany Zeppelin.

Draw and color your own picture here!